Walk Around

Space Shuttle

By Lou Drendel
Color by Lou Drendel
Illustrated by Ernesto Cumpian

Walk Around Number 20

squadron/signal publications

Introduction

The Space Shuttle Orbiter realizes the dream of a reusable manned spacecraft, whose origins date back to the rocket aircraft tested from the late 1940s to the late 1960s. These aircraft began with the Bell X-1 (originally XS-1), which made the first supersonic flight on 14 October 1947. Bell's X-2 was the first to reach Mach 3 on 27 September 1956. The rocket aircraft program reached its climax with the North American X-15, the first winged aircraft to fly into space and land on a runway. In an 11-minute flight on 22 August 1963, the X-15 reached an altitude of 354,200 feet (107,960 м) and achieved a speed of 3794 mph (6105.7 кмн) — Mach 5.58.

Despite the X-15's success, expendable rockets carrying non-aerodynamic spacecraft were the choice of both the Americans and the Soviets during the race to the Moon in the 1960s. The Boeing X-20 Dyna-Soar (Dynamic Soaring) was an early attempt to develop a reusable aerospace aircraft, although this was to be launched by an expendable rocket. The X-20 was cancelled during 1963 after four years of development.

Martin pursued the lifting body (wingless) concept of aerospace vehicles, beginning with the unmanned X-23 hypersonic (Mach 5) test craft. The X-23 was followed by the X-24A manned lifting body, which explored a lifting body's low speed handling characteristics between 1969 and 1971. The X-24B continued this program, reaching altitudes in excess 74,000 feet (22,555.2 м) and speed approaching Mach 1.7. Lifting body research was also carried out by the M2 and HL-10 vehicles designed by the National Aeronautics and Space Administration (NASA).

The successful end of the Moon Race with the Soviets combined with turmoil at home and abroad deeply cut into political support for NASA's more ambitious plans. These plans included a permanent Moon base and a manned trip to Mars. One venture which was retained was a reusable Earth-to-orbit 'space truck.' NASA requested preliminary designs from four companies during 1969 for what would be christened the Space Transportation System (STS), soon to be known as the Space Shuttle.

NASA selected Rockwell International's design, and the first Space Shuttle was rolled out of the company's Palmdale, California plant on 17 September 1976. This test vehicle, named ENTERPRISE, was employed in atmospheric flight tests of the Shuttle concept during 1977. During five successful tests, ENTERPRISE was carried up on a modified Boeing 747 airliner and released to land on Earth. This vehicle was subsequently used for ground testing of the Shuttle system and facilities.

Rockwell would build five operational Shuttles, beginning with COLUMBIA. This vehicle made the first Shuttle space flight on the STS-1 mission of 12-14 April 1981. CHALLENGER, DISCOVERY, and ATLANTIS would follow COLUMBIA into service over the next four years. CHALLENGER was lost in an explosion soon after the launch of STS-51-L on 28 January 1986, killing all seven astronauts aboard. The Shuttle fleet was grounded for two years while the vehicles and associated systems were modified to prevent a similar occurrence. A fifth operational Shuttle, ENDEAVOUR, was completed during 1991 to take CHALLENGER's place. Since resuming flights in 1988, the Space Shuttle fleet has carried astronauts into space and back without accident.

The 93rd Shuttle mission during December of 1998 saw ENDEAVOUR deliver the first US-built section of the International Space Station (ISS). The coming years will see the Shuttles deliver more sections of this station for assembly in orbit, followed in due course by flights of occupants to and from the ISS. The four Orbiters in service continue to fulfill NASA's objectives of a true Space Transportation System.

(Previous Page) DISCOVERY lifts off on 2 June 1998 from Pad 39A at the Kennedy Space Center, Florida on the 91st Shuttle mission. This mission featured the final Shuttle docking with the Russian Space Station MIR. The STS (Space Transportation System)-91 crew consisted of: Commander Charles Precourt, Pilot Dominic Gorie, and Mission Specialists Wendy Lawrence, Franklin Chang-Diaz, Janet Lynn Kavandi, and Valery Victorovich Ryumin. Astronaut Andrew Thomas returned to earth aboard DISCOVERY after a four month stay on MIR. (NASA)

ISBN 0-89747-406-6

If you have any photographs of aircraft, armor, soldiers or ships of any nation, particularly wartime snapshots, why not share them with us and help make Squadron/Signal's books all the more interesting and complete in the future. Any photograph sent to us will be copied and the original returned. The donor will be fully credited for any photos used. Please send them to:

Squadron/Signal Publications, Inc.
1115 Crowley Drive
Carrollton, TX 75011-5010

Если у вас есть фотографии самолётов, вооружения, солдат или кораблей любой страны, особенно, снимки времён войны, поделитесь с нами и помогите сделать новые книги издательства Эскадрон/Сигнал ещё интереснее. Мы переснимем ваши фотографии и вернём оригиналы. Имена приславших снимки будут сопровождать все опубликованные фотографии. Пожалуйста, присылайте фотографии по адресу:

Squadron/Signal Publications, Inc.
1115 Crowley Drive
Carrollton, TX 75011-5010

軍用機、装甲車両、兵士、軍艦などの写真を所持しておられる方はいらっしゃいませんか？どの国のものでも結構です。作戦中に撮影されたものが特に良いのです。Squadron/Signal社の出版する刊行物において、このような写真は内容を一層充実し、興味深くすることができます。当方にお送り頂いた写真は、複写の後お返しいたします。出版物中に写真を使用した場合は、必ず提供者のお名前を明記させて頂きます。お写真は下記にご送付ください。

Squadron/Signal Publications, Inc.
1115 Crowley Drive
Carrollton, TX 75011-5010

(Front Cover) The Space Shuttle DISCOVERY lifts off from Launch Complex 39 of the Kennedy Space Center, Florida. The three Space Shuttle Main Engines and the two Solid Rocket Boosters combine to produce 3.78 million lbs (1.7 million кG) of thrust at liftoff. The black heat resistant material immediately behind the gray wing leading edges was replaced with white material on all Shuttles except COLUMBIA during major overhauls.

Acknowledgements

The author is grateful for the assistance and encouragement of GEN Don Kutyna, USAF (Ret).
(Back Cover) The payload bay doors of the Shuttle Orbiter ATLANTIS are opened while the vehicle is in Earth orbit. The Shuttle Remote Manipulator System (SRMS) arm is extended in the forward area of the payload bay, while two pallets for deploying satellites are housed in the aft end of the bay.

The North American X-15 was the first winged spacecraft to land under a pilot's control. The three X-15s produced made 199 flights between 17 September 1959 and 24 October 1968. Eight X-15 flights qualified as 'astro-flights' — flights above 50 miles/80.5 KM.

Shuttles

ENTERPRISE (OV-101) — This test vehicle was originally to be named CONSTITUTION, in honor of the Bicentennial of the US Constitution. This Shuttle's name was changed as a result of a campaign by dedicated fans of the television series 'Star Trek', who lobbied for ENTERPRISE in honor of Captain Kirk's starship. After being rolled out 17 September 1976, ENTERPRISE made eight captive and five free flights before being retired to the National Air and Space Museum in Washington.

COLUMBIA (OV-102) — The oldest orbiter in the fleet is named after the sloop captained by Robert Gray, who navigated the river ultimately named for his ship in 1792. Gray also made the first American circumnavigation of the globe in this ship. This orbiter was rolled out on 8 March 1979 and made its first flight (STS-1) on 12 April 1981. This Shuttle underwent an extensive retrofit program during 1992. As of mid-1999, COLUMBIA had made 26 flights.

CHALLENGER (OV-099) — CHALLENGER was named after an American naval research vessel from the 1870s. Built as a high fidelity structural test vehicle, it rolled out on 14 February 1978. After 11 months of intensive vibration testing in a 43 ton (39 MT) steel test rig, CHALLENGER converted to a fully rated orbiter. The converted Shuttle was rolled out on 30 June 1982, and made its first flight on 4 April 1983 (STS-6). CHALLENGER was lost during the launch of STS-51-L (its 10th mission) on 28 January 1986.

DISCOVERY (OV-103) — DISCOVERY was named for the second of two ships used by British explorer James Cook during the 1770s. This Shuttle benefited from experience gained in operation of previous Shuttles, weighing 6870 lbs (3116.2 KG) less at rollout than COLUMBIA. Rollout occurred on 16 October 1983, with the first flight on 30 August 1984 (STS-41-D). Through mid-1999, DISCOVERY had made 26 flights.

ATLANTIS (OV-104) — ATLANTIS is named for the primary research vessel of the Woods Hole Oceanographic Institute in Massachusetts from 1930 to 1966. This vehicle rolled out weighing almost 7000 lbs (3175.2 KG) less than COLUMBIA and was constructed with a 49.5% reduction in the man-hours required to build COLUMBIA. Rollout occurred on 6 March

ENTERPRISE (OV-101) was the first Space Shuttle. Although this test vehicle never flew in space, ENTERPRISE proved the glide to land concept of the Shuttle design.

1985, with the first flight (STS-51-J) taking place on 3 October 1985. ATLANTIS made 20 flights before being returned to Palmdale for upgrades during 1997.

ENDEAVOUR (OV-105) — ENDEAVOUR is named for James Cook's first ship, in which he sailed the South Pacific during the 1770s. The name was chosen through a national competition among elementary and secondary school children. President George Bush announced the winning name in 1989. ENDEAVOUR was assembled using many of the spares manufactured as backups in case of an accident. It rolled out on 25 April 1991, and made its first flight on 7 May 1992 (STS-49). Through the middle of 1999, ENDEAVOUR had made 13 flights.

Several cast members from the television show 'Star Trek' attended the rollout of its namesake, the Shuttle ENTERPRISE, on 17 September 1976. The guests included (L-R): NASA Administrator Dr. James B. Fletcher, DeForest Kelly, George Takei, James Doohan, Nichelle Nichols, Leonard Nimoy, 'Star Trek' Producer and Creator Gene Roddenberry, an unidentified NASA official, and Walter Koenig. (NASA)

(Below) CHALLENGER (OV-099) is rolled into the Mate/Demate Facility at NASA's Dryden Flight Research Facility, located at Edwards Air Force Base. The facility is used to install or remove the Shuttle from the 747 SCA. Ferry flights are conducted with a large tail fairing to eliminate turbulent airflow around the 747's tail. (NASA)

(Above) ENTERPRISE was used to conduct Approach and Landing Tests (ALT) at Edwards Air Force Base, California during 1977. These tests also qualified the Shuttle Carrier Aircraft (SCA), a converted Boeing 747 (NASA 905). A T-38 chase aircraft accompanies ENTERPRISE and the SCA. (NASA via Robert F. Dorr.)

(Below) CHALLENGER rides on the Boeing 747 SCA for a ferry flight. The SCA was modified with 10-ft (3 M) by 20-ft (6 M) vertical fins added to the horizontal stabilizers. These added fins enhanced directional stability for the Shuttle/SCA combination. The combined takeoff weight of these aircraft is 713,000 lbs (323,417 KG). (NASA via Robert F. Dorr)

(Below) A spent Solid Rocket Booster (SRB) is lifted in a hoisting slip at Cape Canaveral Air Station, Florida. The reusable Thiokol SRBs are jettisoned at two minutes seven seconds into the flight and splash down 6 minutes 44 seconds after launch. Each SRB at splashdown weighs 165,000 lbs (74,844 KG). (NASA)

(Above) CHALLENGER leaves Palmdale, California for Edwards AFB on 1 July 1982. Prior to achieving flight status on that date, this former structural test vehicle underwent extensive vibration testing. Testing was conducted with 256 hydraulic jacks in a specially built jig. The 38-mile (61.2-KM) trip takes up to 12 hours of careful driving!

(Below) FREEDOM STAR, one of NASA's two solid rocket booster recovery ships, tows a barge containing an External Tank (ET) into Port Canaveral. The ETs are manufactured by Lockheed Martin in New Orleans and moved to the Kennedy Space Center via barge. The other recovery ship is named LIBERTY STAR. (NASA)

Space Shuttle Development

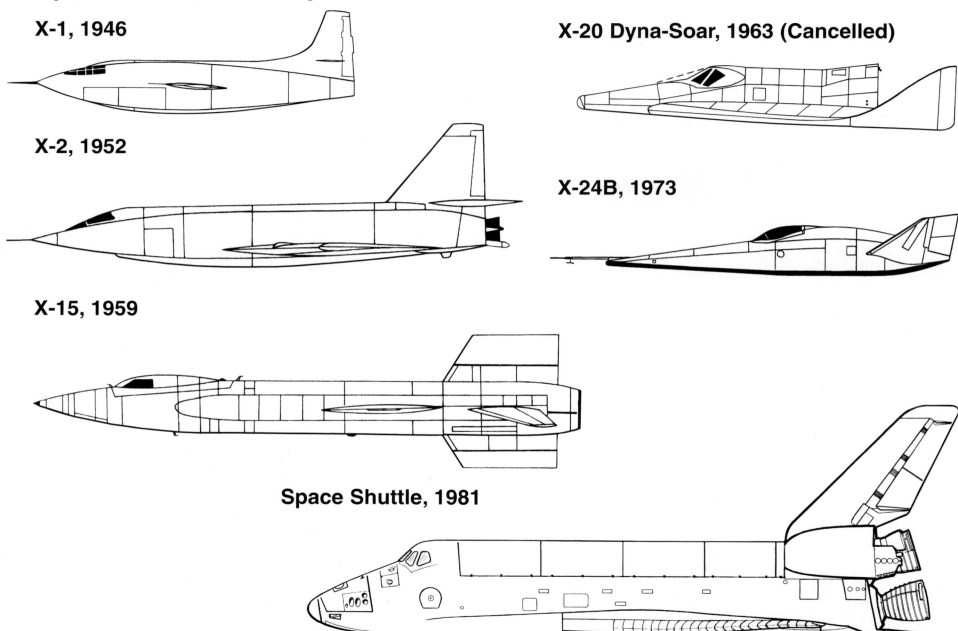

X-1, 1946

X-20 Dyna-Soar, 1963 (Cancelled)

X-2, 1952

X-24B, 1973

X-15, 1959

Space Shuttle, 1981

ENTERPRISE separates from the 747 SCA on its final free flight on 26 October 1977. The rear fuselage fairing was removed for this flight and dummy main engine and Orbiting Maneuver System (OMS) engine bells were installed to verify the Shuttle's handling under these conditions. (NASA)

CHALLENGER, aboard the 747 SCA, climbs out from Edwards AFB enroute to the Kennedy Space Center (KSC) on 13 August 1982. The 747 was highly instrumented to monitor stress on the airframe during the Shuttle carrying flights. The 747/Shuttle combination first flew on 18 February 1977. (NASA via Robert F. Dorr)

COLUMBIA (OV-102), aboard the SCA, returns to KSC on 6 April 1982 following the STS-3 mission. The Shuttle had landed on 30 March at White Sands Missile Range, New Mexico after the original landing site at Edwards AFB was flooded by heavy rain. (NASA)

The 747 SCA with COLUMBIA clears the KSC runway on 25 November 1981 upon returning from Edwards AFB following STS-2. The special Shuttle mounting brackets are anchored by reinforcements on the 747's fuselage. (NASA)

ATLANTIS is moved from the Orbiter Processing Facility (OPF) to the Vehicle Assembly Building (VAB) at the Kennedy Space Center. The elements of the Orbiter's Thermal Protection System (TPS) result in the vehicle's 'color' scheme. The off-white payload bay and wing surfaces are covered with Nomex Felt Reusable Surface Insulation (FRSI). The brighter white material consists of Advanced Flexible Reusable Surface Insulation (AFRSI) blankets. Gray Reinforced Carbon-Carbon (RCC) material is used on the nose and wing leading edges, while the black areas are High-Temperature Reusable Surface Insulation (HRSI) tiles. (NASA)

ATLANTIS is rolled out of OPF-3 on 11 August 1997, prior to STS-86. The openings of the Space Shuttle Main Engines and the Orbital Maneuvering System engine bells have red covers to prevent Foreign Object Damage (FOD) during maintenance. The refurbishment of an Orbiter takes approximately 2/3rd of the time between launches. The remaining time is used to assemble the launch package — Orbiter, External Tank, and Solid Rocket Boosters — in the VAB and transport it to the launch pad. Yellow lines on the pavement assist OPF crews in maneuvering Shuttles in and out of the hangars. The narrow slot above the OPF opening allows clearance for the Shuttle's vertical stabilizer. (NASA)

(Below) ENTERPRISE is moved into the Mate/Demate Device at the Kennedy Space Center. This is one of three such devices — the other two are at Edwards AFB and at Vandenberg AFB, California. Three 43-ton (39 мт) capacity hoists are used to lift the Shuttle into position for placement on the 747 Shuttle Carrier Aircraft (SCA). (NASA)

(Above) CHALLENGER and the 747 Shuttle Carrier Aircraft (NASA 905) fly past downtown Houston while en route from Edwards AFB to KSC after STS-6 on 16 April 1983. The 10-ft (3 м) by 20-ft (6 м) horizontal stabilizer tip fins provide additional stability to the 747 when the Shuttle is carried. (NASA)

(Below) A Stiff-Leg Derrick System is used to remove ENTERPRISE from the 747 SCA at the Marshall Space Flight Center in Huntsville, Alabama. The derrick system is portable and would be used to retrieve orbiters which might be forced to land at one of 47 contingency landing sites worldwide. (NASA)

(Below) An SCA 747 and COLUMBIA are towed into position at the KSC Mate/Demate facility. The various patches on the Orbiter are sealants used to protect COLUMBIA during the 2400 mile (3862 km) flight from Dryden Flight Research Center. The 747 retained the basic color scheme of its previous operator — American Airlines. (NASA)

(Above) The 747/Shuttle combination — called 'The World's Largest Biplane' by 747 pilot Fitzhugh Fulton — touches down at the Kennedy Space Center (KSC) on 24 March 1979. This date marked the first landing of the 747 with Orbiter at KSC. This combination has a landing speed of 143 mph (230.2 kmh). (NASA)

(Below) ENTERPRISE glides back to Edwards AFB during its second free flight on 13 September 1977. The large air data probe on the nose was only carried during these free flights to verify subsonic airworthiness. Other flight regimes required verification in wind tunnels prior to the first Shuttle launch on 12 April 1981. (NASA)

COLUMBIA is rolled out of the Vehicle Assembly Building (VAB) on 23 March 1998 for the STS-90 mission. All Shuttle missions after STS-7 during 1983 have used the orange light-weight External Tank (ET), whose inert weight of 66,000 lbs (29,938 KG) is 11,000 lbs (4990 KG) lighter than the previous used ET. The ET's fully loaded weight is 1,665,607 lbs (755,519.3 KG). (NASA)

The Lockheed Martin External Tank (ET) attached to COLUMBIA for STS-90 is 153.8 feet (46.9 M) long, and 27.6 feet (8.4 M) in diameter. The Thiokol Solid Rocket Boosters (SRBs) are attached to the mobile launch platform and carry the entire weight of the launch package — Orbiter, ET, and SRBs. The SRBs are the largest solid-propellant motors ever flown and are the first such motors designed for reuse. (NASA)

CHALLENGER is positioned on Launch Pad 39A prior to the STS-6 mission in April of 1983. Launch Complex 39 Pads A and B were originally designed to support the Apollo program and were modified for Shuttle operations. Tail Service Masts on the Mobile Launch Platform provide propellant loading and electrical power for the Orbiter. The Fixed Service Structure (FSS) includes the Orbiter Access Arm to allow crew entry and exit from the Shuttle, and External Tank electrical and venting connections. The FSS is topped by an 80-foot (24.4 M) tall Fiberglas lightning rod, grounded by 1100-foot (335.3 M) long cables anchored north and south of the pad. The Rotating Service Structure next to the FSS contains the Payload Changeout Room for Shuttle payloads, along with fluid and gas connections to the Shuttle. (NASA)

Space Shuttle
with External Tank and Solid Rocket Boosters

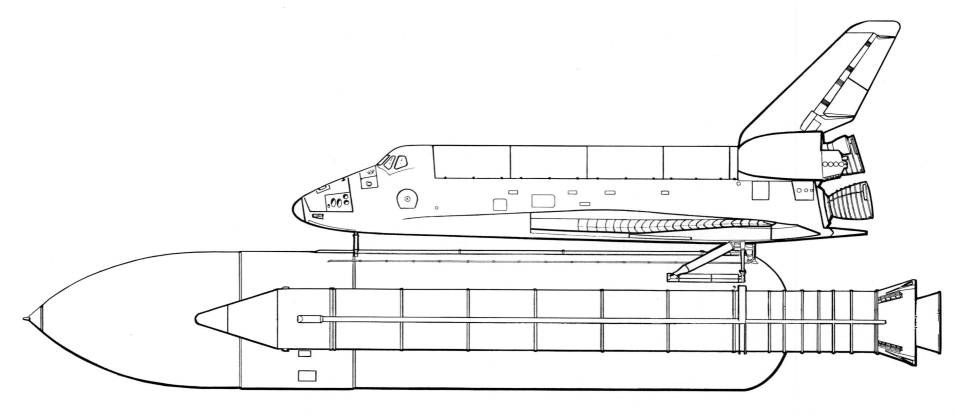

Orbiter Specifications (For ENDEAVOUR, OV-105)
Length................................122.17 ft (37.24 м)
Wingspan...........................78.06 ft (23.79 м)
Height................................56.58 ft (17.25 м)
Empty Weight....................151,205 lbs (68,586.6 кɢ)
Main Engines.....................Three Rocketdyne Block 2A SSME, each with a sea level thrust
    of 375,000 lbs (170,100 кɢ)
Maximum Payload............55,250 lbs (25,061.4 кɢ)
Payload Bay Dimentions..15 ft by 60 ft (4.6 м by 18.3 м)
Crossrange.......................1085 nautical miles (2009.4 кm)
Crew..................................Seven (Commander, Pilot, two Mission Specialists, and three
    Payload Specialists)

Solid Rocket Booster Specifications
Length................................149.6 ft (45.6 м)
Diameter............................12.17 ft (3.71 м)
Weight...............................139,490 lbs (63,272.7 кɢ)
Thrust................................3,485,000 lbs (1,580,796 кɢ)

External Tank Specifications
Length................................153.8 ft (46.9 м)
Diameter............................27.6 ft (8.4 м)
Empty Weight....................66,000 lbs (29,938 кɢ)

The **SPACEHAB** payload for STS-89 — launched during January of 1998 — is installed in the Payload Changeout Room at Launch Pad 39A. The Rotating Service Structure (RSS) will be rotated through 120˚ until it is flush with **ENDEAVOUR's** payload bay. This allowed the **SPACEHAB** to be loaded under contamination-free 'clean room' conditions. (NASA)

COLUMBIA is prepared for the launch of STS-90 from Pad 39B in April of 1998. The RSS was rolled back at T-minus 11 hours to indicate an imminent launch. The 500,000 gallons (1,892,700 L) of liquid hydrogen and liquid oxygen are loaded into the External Tank after RSS rollback. (NASA)

DISCOVERY clears the tower on the launch of STS-91 on 2 June 1998. The Solid Rocket Boosters (SRBs) generate a combined thrust of 6,970,000 lbs (3,161,592 KG) — 71% of the thrust needed for liftoff. The SRBs are jettisoned at 150,000 feet (45,720 M) before descending by parachute into the ocean 122 nautical miles downrange. (NASA)

ATLANTIS lifts off trailing thick smoke from the SRBs and steam from cooling water. The Rotating Service Structure is positioned in front of the Fixed Service Structure. The two SRBs and the three Space Shuttle Main Engines combine to produce 8.1 million lbs (3.67 million KG) of thrust at liftoff. (NASA)

17

A Crawler/Transporter moves a Mobile Launch Platform (MLP) with COLUMBIA up the incline to Pad 39A on 16 February 1982. The Marion Power Shovel Company of Marion, Ohio built two Crawler/Transporters (CTs) during the 1960s for the Apollo Program. These CTs remain the only machines of their size and kind in the world. Two 2750 horsepower diesel engines drive the 3000-ton (2721.6 мт) machines at a maximum loaded speed of one mph (1.6 кмн). The MLP remains level during the move due to the transporter's stability system. This system's effectiveness is such that the tip of the External Tank does not move more than the diameter of a basketball during the trip up the incline. (NASA)

The Shuttle launch package — ENTERPRISE, External Tank (ET), and Solid Rocket Boosters — moves out of the Vehicle Assembly Building on 1 May 1979 for the first movement to Launch Pad 39A. The ET attachment strut is connected to the Orbiter by explosive bolts. The tank separates from the Orbiter 18 seconds after main engine cut off, and after separation follows a ballistic trajectory before impact in the Indian Ocean. (NASA)

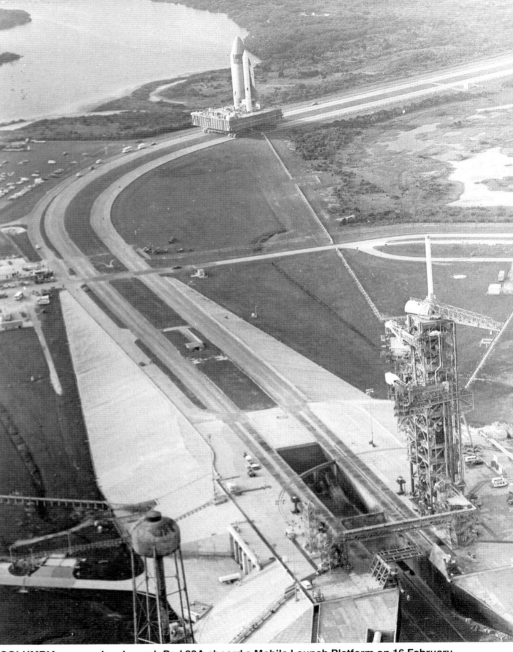

COLUMBIA approaches Launch Pad 39A aboard a Mobile Launch Platform on 16 February 1982. The Crawler/Transporter required 5.5 hours to transport this Launch Package the 3.5 miles (5.6 KM) from the VAB. The tank next to the launch pad contains 300,000 gallons (1,135,620 L) of water for the Sound Suppression Water System, which protects the launch structure from the intense sound pressure of liftoff. (NASA)

The fuselage of CHALLENGER takes shape at the Rockwell International factory in Palmdale, California. The lower half of the forward fuselage and the wings have been joined to the mid-fuselage. The pressurized crew compartment is installed into the lower forward fuselage prior to installation of the upper forward fuselage. The skins attached to the frames are integral-machined aluminum and aluminum honeycomb sandwich panels. Construction of CHALLENGER as a Structural Test Article (STA-099) began during 1975 and was completed in 1978. (Rockwell)

CHALLENGER is rolled out at Palmdale on 30 June 1982 with the ferry flight tail fairing installed. Rockwell's original $2.6 billion contract for the Shuttle had authorized the building of two static-test articles (MPTA-098 and STA-099) and two initial flight-test vehicles (OV-101 and OV-102). A decision in 1978 not to modify ENTERPRISE (OV-101) from her Approach and Landing Test (ALT) configuration would have left COLUMBIA (OV-102) as the only operational Orbiter vehicle. NASA awarded Rockwell a supplemental contract on 29 January 1979 to convert CHALLENGER from the STA-099 test vehicle into a space rated Orbiter (OV-099). (NASA)

COLUMBIA inches out of the Vehicle Assembly Building (VAB) aboard a Mobile Launch Platform. The VAB at the Kennedy Space Center was built during the 1960s to support the Apollo Moon missions. The building is 525 feet (157.5 M) tall, 716 feet (214.8 M) long, and 518 feet (155.4 M) wide. Construction of the VAB required 98,590 tons (89,500 MT) of steel and 65,000 cubic yards (5221.8 M³) of concrete. (NASA via Robert F. Dorr)

External Tank

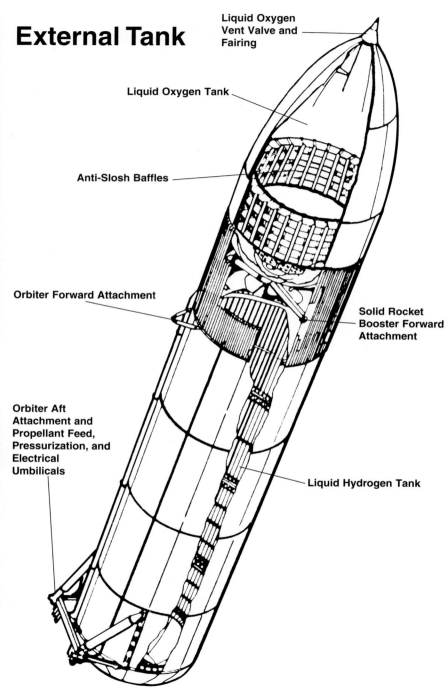

Liquid Oxygen Vent Valve and Fairing

Liquid Oxygen Tank

Anti-Slosh Baffles

Orbiter Forward Attachment

Solid Rocket Booster Forward Attachment

Orbiter Aft Attachment and Propellant Feed, Pressurization, and Electrical Umbilicals

Liquid Hydrogen Tank

Solid Rocket Booster

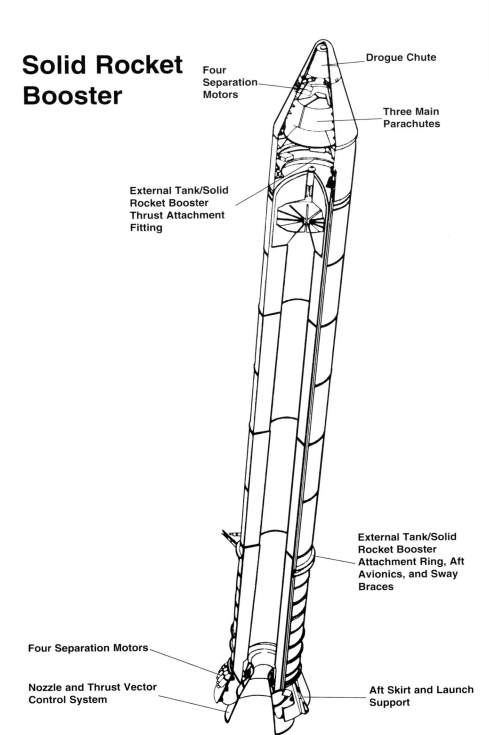

Drogue Chute

Four Separation Motors

Three Main Parachutes

External Tank/Solid Rocket Booster Thrust Attachment Fitting

External Tank/Solid Rocket Booster Attachment Ring, Aft Avionics, and Sway Braces

Four Separation Motors

Aft Skirt and Launch Support

Nozzle and Thrust Vector Control System

The External Tank is mated to the Solid Rocket Boosters (SRBs) in the VAB prior to their mating with the Orbiter COLUMBIA. Explosive bolts attach the SRBs to the Mobile Launch Platform (MLP). These bolts are blown off at launch. The foreground plumbing is part of the MLP. (NASA)

Two forward Reaction Control System (RCS) primary thrusters are mounted on each side of the Orbiter's nose. Three small vernier thrusters for minute control are mounted near the main thrusters. Six additional primary thrusters are mounted on top of the nose. The Marquardt RCS provides attitude control and translation along the pitch, roll, and yaw axes during the flight phases of orbit insertion, orbit, and reentry. Black high-temperature tiles are used in areas on the upper forward fuselage. White Low-Temperature Reusable Surface Insulation tiles are used in selected areas of the forward, mid, and aft fuselage. These tiles protect areas where reentry temperatures are below 1200° F (649° C). (NASA)

(Above) Plugs inside these Reaction Control System (RCS) thruster exhausts are attached to thruster Foreign Object Damage (FOD) covers, which protect the thruster openings during maintenance. The Shuttle RCS consists of 38 primary thrusters and six vernier thrusters for attitude control. Propellants for the thrusters are Monomethyl Hydrazine (MNH) and Nitrogen Tetroxide (N_2O_4). (John Rippinger)

(Above Right) The Purge and Checkout Panel is located on the port side of the forward RCS Module. High-temperature tiles protect this panel during missions, however, a black plastic sheet covers the panel during maintenance. (John Rippinger)

(Right) One of the starboard forward RCS thrusters is covered with plastic sheeting during Orbiter maintenance. The forward RCS module contains 14 primary and two vernier thrusters. The Purge and Checkout Panel, covered with plastic sheet, is located under the lower vernier thruster exhaust. (John Rippinger)

25

The nose landing gear of COLUMBIA is raised off the floor of the Vehicle Assembly Building (VAB) on 19 May 1982. The Michelin nose landing gear tires are 32 x 8.8 with an inflation pressure of 300 psi. COLUMBIA was originally delivered with nose gear steering, however, this proved ineffective during high speed maneuvers. That feature was deactivated from COLUMBIA after STS-4, and a new nose gear steering system was installed for STS-32. This new system is also installed on the other operational Orbiters. (NASA)

The forward attachment point for the External Tank is placed behind the Orbiter's nose landing gear doors. Red protective caps cover the attachment brackets during Orbiter maintenance. High-Temperature Reusable Surface Insulation tiles vary in thickness from one inch (2.54 cm) to five inches (12.7 cm), depending upon the heat load encountered during reentry. These tiles are nominally six by six inches (15.2 by 15.2 cm). (John Rippinger)

Nose Landing Gear

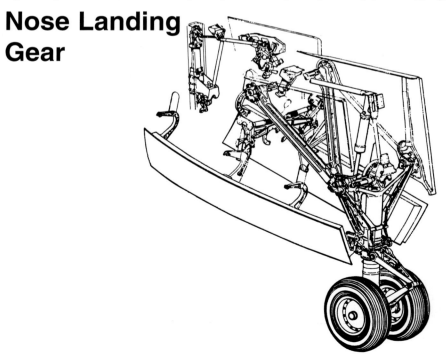

The crew module 'Beanie Cap' for ATLANTIS is prepared for installation on the forward fuselage. Openings for the windshield and overhead windows will be cut out once this section is installed. The 'Beanie Cap' is attached to the forward fuselage at four points and then welded to create a pressure-tight vessel. (Rockwell)

Forward Reaction Control System

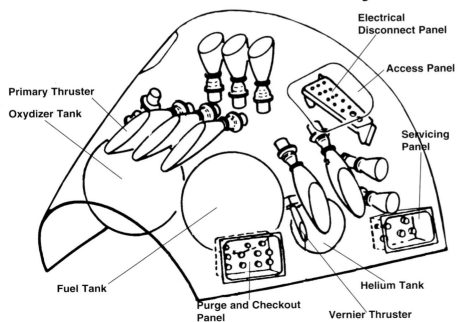

Electrical Disconnect Panel

Access Panel

Primary Thruster

Oxydizer Tank

Servicing Panel

Fuel Tank

Helium Tank

Purge and Checkout Panel

Vernier Thruster

The thermal barrier of ceramic alumini borosilica is installed on DISCOVERY's crew module in 1982. Window panes have been fitted into the windshield openings. The innermost panes are of 0.625 in (1.6 cm) thick tempered alumino-silicate glass, while the outer panes are of fused silica glass ranging from 1.3 in (3.3 cm) to 0.625 in (1.6 cm) thick. (Rockwell)

COLUMBIA is moved from the Palmdale factory to Edwards AFB on a heavy-duty transporter on 8 March 1979. The windshield windows are covered for protection during the move. The thermal tiles covering the Shuttle are designed to withstand the cold soak of −250° F (-121° C) in space to the nearly 3000° F (1649° C) heat of reentry. The tiles are reusable for up to 100 missions with refurbishment. (NASA)

STS-76 Mission Commander Kevin Chilton (left) and Pilot Richard Searfoss aboard ATLANTIS during the Terminal Countdown Demonstration Test (TCDT) — a launch dress rehearsal — on 6 March 1996. Extensive flight crew checklists are attached to the windshield for ready reference. Three monochrome Cathode Ray Tubes (CRTs) dominate the center of the instrument panel and display flight information for the pilots. Other flight control instruments are on the instrument panel, while the flight computer and navigation aids console is placed between the pilots' seats. Additional systems controls are mounted in the overhead console. (NASA)

STS-85 Commander Curtis L. Brown, Jr. sits in the port pilot's seat on board DISCOVERY during the TCDT on 23 July 1997. After the loss of CHALLENGER on 28 January 1986, NASA returned to the practice of launch and recovery in full pressure suits, including integral parachute and survival gear. Heads-Up Displays (HUDs) were factory installed on all orbiters except COLUMBIA, which had HUDs retrofitted during 1983. (NASA)

STS-85 Pilot Ken V. Rominger participates in the TCDT aboard DISCOVERY. The varied thickness pads behind the pilot's helmet cushion the head and neck from the g-loads of launch. The Rotational Hand Controller between each pilot's legs controls the Shuttle's rotation about three axes: roll, pitch, and yaw. The fisheye camera lens results in the curvature of some Flight Deck panels. (NASA)

Most of the instrumentation has been installed in the flight deck of DISCOVERY (OV-103) during the Shuttle's construction in May of 1983. Covers have been placed over all windshield windows except the center panel. Pedals control the rudder during atmospheric flight after reentry and also include wheel brakes. Heads-Up Displays (HUDs) have not yet been installed into the instrument shroud openings. The side panels control various systems, including environmental, hydraulics, landing gear, and electrical power. Future plans call for the electro-mechanical flight instruments to be replaced with Liquid Crystal Displays (LCDs). (NASA)

Cathode Ray Tubes (CRTs) and keyboards have not yet been installed in the flight deck of ENTERPRISE (OV-101) during construction. The control sticks are articulated for right hand operation and control the elevons during atmospheric flight. Upper windows — only installed on this Shuttle — have been installed. Lockheed zero-zero ejection seats have not yet been fitted to ENTERPRISE. (NASA)

Flight Deck

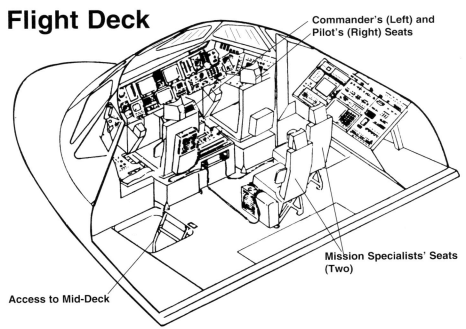

Commander's (Left) and Pilot's (Right) Seats

Mission Specialists' Seats (Two)

Access to Mid-Deck

Commander John Young (left) and Pilot Bob Crippen conduct a mission simulation aboard COLUMBIA on 10 October 1983. The pilots sit in Lockheed zero-zero ejection seats, which were deactivated after STS-4 and removed after STS-9. Overhead consoles include controls for the Reaction Control System (RCS). A fire extinguisher is mounted behind the Pilot's seat. (NASA)

The STS-6 crew train in the Shuttle simulator at the Johnson Space Center in Houston, Texas. This simulator is an exact duplicate of the Shuttle flight deck. This crew — Commander and Pilot in front, Mission Specialists in back — wears the launch uniform used from STS-5 during 1982 until the loss of CHALLENGER on 28 January 1986. (NASA)

(Above Left) The STS-71 crew, commanded by Robert 'Hoot' Gibson, practices countdown procedures aboard ATLANTIS on Pad 39A. Guards surrounding the overhead toggle switches prevent accidental switch operation. The flight crew's seats adjust vertically (10 inches/25.4 CM) and longitudinally (5 inches/12.7 CM) via a three-position switch on the seat pan. STS-71, launched on 27 June 1995, docked with the Russian Space Station MIR before returning to earth on 7 July. (NASA)

(Above) STS-75 Pilot Scott J. 'Doc' Horowitz and Mission Specialists Jeffrey A. Hoffman (center) and Maurizio Cheli aboard COLUMBIA during the Terminal Countdown Demonstration Test (TCDT) on 2 February 1996. The overhead windows above the aft flight deck station are used for orbital rendezvous. The cloth inner helmets include radio and intercom microphones. Individual checklists and notepads are mounted on knee-boards for the crewmember's use while seated. (NASA)

(Left) STS-71 Pilot Charles Precourt and Mission Specialists Ellen Baker (in background) and Gregory Harbaugh conduct the TCDT on 25 May 1995. The helmets include a dark outer visor for protection from intense sunlight and a clear inner visor. The crew compartment is pressurized to 14.7 pounds per square inch absolute (psia) and is maintained at an 80% nitrogen and 20% oxygen composition by the environmental control system. The total crew compartment volume, with airlock installed, is 2325 cubic feet (65.8 M³). (NASA)

STS-75 crew members (from left) Pilot Scott J. 'Doc' Horowitz, Mission Commander Andrew M. Allen, and Mission Specialists Jeffrey A. Hoffman and Maurizio Cheli relax during the TCDT aboard COLUMBIA. An ascent checklist is clipped to Hoffman's left thigh for ready reference during the ascent phase of the flight, while other notes are on his right thigh. The pressure suits include parachutes on the back and survival equipment. Additional Mission Specialists Franklin R. Chang-Diaz, Claude Nicollier, and Umberto Guidoni were seated in the lower crew compartment. Covers marked REMOVE BEFORE FLIGHT were placed over the rear windows for this test. (NASA)

STS-85 Payload Commander N. Jan Davis (left) and Mission Specialist Robert L. Curbeam, Jr. conduct the TCDT aboard DISCOVERY. Each crewperson wears kneeboards on both legs, and Curbeam wears a digital watch on his wrist. The several checklists each have their own tether to contain them under weightlessness in orbit. Aft flight deck displays and controls are located on the panel next to Davis' seat and at the aft station. (NASA)

Mission Commander 'Hoot' Gibson floats in COLUMBIA's aft flight deck area during STS-61-C on 15 January 1986. The black grip on the aft mission station is the hand controller used to fly the Shuttle during orbital rendezvous maneuvers. The overhead windows assist the flight crews in these maneuvers. (NASA)

Aft Mission Station

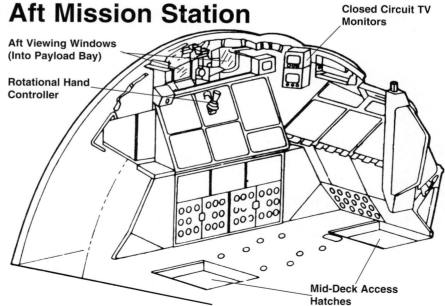

Mission Specialists (from left) Nikolai M. Budarin, Anatoly Y. Solovyev, and Bonnie J. Dunbar settle in their launch positions on ATLANTIS' mid-deck prior to STS-71 in 1995. The airlock door is located behind Budarin's seat. The mid-deck seats will be stowed once the Shuttle is on orbit, allowing access to the airlock and the MIR Space Station docking module. Budarin and Solovyev were the first Russians to fly on the Shuttle. (NASA)

Mid-Deck

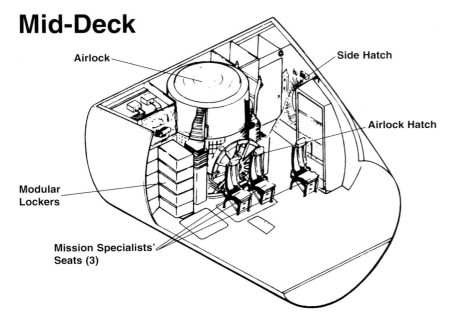

Airlock

Side Hatch

Airlock Hatch

Modular Lockers

Mission Specialists' Seats (3)

STS-89 Mission Specialists (from left) Andrew Thomas, Salizhan Sharipov, and James Reilly sit in the mid-deck launch position aboard ENDEAVOUR during the Terminal Countdown Demonstration Test (TCDT) on 10 January 1998. Foam padding has been taped over an avionics equipment box to prevent damage during ascent. A curtain directly behind the seats hides the airlock, which allows astronauts to spacewalk. (NASA)

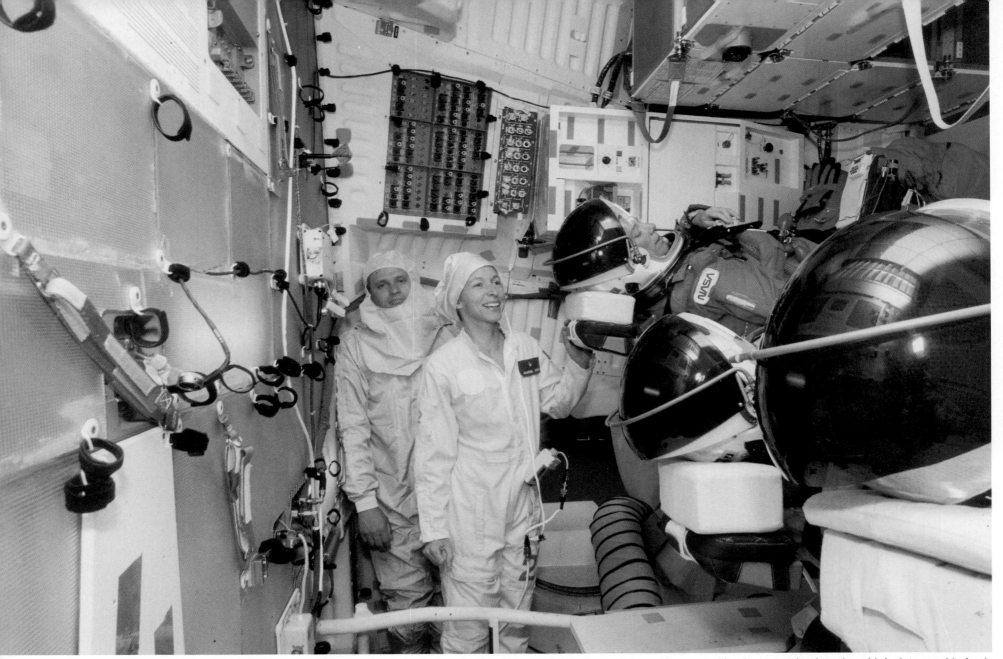

STS-71 crewmembers conduct pre-mission countdown procedures testing in the mid-deck of ATLANTIS on 25 May 1995. They are assisted by NASA Astronaut Marsha S. Ivins (second from left) and MIR-19 backup crewmember Yuri I. Onufrienko (left). Nylon fastening loops on the aft wall are used to secure equipment for use during the flight. The side hatch in the background is open with a hose running into the mid-deck to provide fresh air during this exercise. The hatch employs a pressure seal compressed by the latch mechanisms when this hatch is locked closed. The side hatch weighs 294 lbs (133.4 KG) (NASA)

(Above) A wire harness has been installed in the mid-fuselage of DISCOVERY (OV-103) at Rockwell's Palmdale plant during 1982. Temporary work platforms allow workers access to aft fuselage areas. Electrical power carried by these wires is provided by three nose-mounted fuel cells generating up to 24 kilowatts. The Convair Aerospace Division of General Dynamics, subcontracting to Rockwell, produced the mid-fuselage sections in San Diego. (Rockwell)

(Above Right) Two workers assemble portions of the aft fuselage of ATLANTIS (OV-104) during 1982. The truss-type internal structure consists of diffusion-bonded elements. These elements transfer the main engine thrust loads to the mid-fuselage and External Tank, which reduces stress to the aft fuselage. The titanium structure is reinforced with tubular struts made of boron-epoxy, which added stiffness while reducing weight. (Rockwell)

(Right) Rockwell workers apply markings to an Orbiter's aft fuselage at Palmdale. Blankets are used while painting to prevent damage to the Orbiter's protective surfaces. The gray NASA 'worm' logo applied to all orbiters would be replaced (except on CHALLENGER, which exploded in 1986) with the traditional NASA 'meatball' emblem in 1997. (NASA)

(Above) COLUMBIA is rolled out of the Rockwell International's Plant 42 at Palmdale on 8 March 1979. The Orbiter is mounted on a special heavy-duty transporter for the 12-hour, 38 mile (61.2 км) trip from Palmdale to Edwards AFB. The aerodynamic fairing has been placed over the engines for COLUMBIA's flight aboard the 747 Shuttle Carrier Aircraft from Edwards to the Kennedy Space Center. (NASA)

(Left) The starboard payload bay door of ATLANTIS (OV-104) is open in Orbiter Processing Facility (OPF) 3 at the Kennedy Space Center on 14 April 1995. In the foreground is the Orbiter Docking System (ODS) which was used for the first docking with the Russian space station MIR. The red and white striped canister at left is a Very High Frequency (VHF) antenna used to communicate with MIR. (US military communications primarily use Ultra High Frequency/UHF.) The Spacelab-MIR module at the far end of the payload bay served as an orbital medical laboratory for joint US-Russian experiments on long-duration spaceflight. Robert L. 'Hoot' Gibson, making his fifth Shuttle flight, commanded STS-71 (27 June to 7 July 1995). The rest of the crew consisted of Pilot Charles Precourt, Payload Commander Ellen S. Baker, and Mission Specialists Gregory Harbaugh and Bonnie Dunbar. Russian Cosmonauts Anatoly Solovyev and Nikolai Budarin flew on ATLANTIS to MIR, while Astronaut Norman Thagard and Cosmonauts Vladimir Dezhurov and Gennady Strekalov left MIR to fly back to Earth on ATLANTIS. (NASA)

The Westar VI communications satellite spins out of its clamshell-doored container aboard CHALLENGER during STS-41-B on 18 May 1984. The Payload Assist Module (PAM) at the base of the satellite contains a rocket to boost Westar VI to its proper orbit. The Shuttle Remote Manipulator System (SRMS), built by Spar Aerospace, Ltd of Canada, is stowed along the port side of the payload bay. (NASA)

CHALLENGER's cargo bay is photographed from the free-flying Shuttle Pallet Satellite (SPAS), which was deployed by the SRMS during STS-7. The payload bay doors remain open during orbit to allow heat to escape from the Orbiter via the radiators inside these doors. The cylinders inside the payload bay contain Get-Away Special experiments carried for a fee payable to NASA. The Ku-band antenna next to the starboard payload bay door is used for rendezvous radar and satellite communications. (NASA)

Shuttle Remote Manipulator System

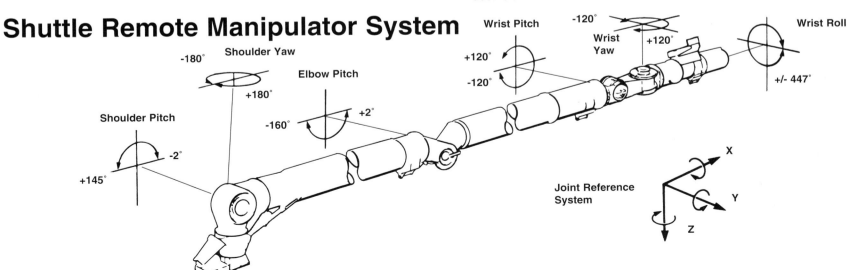

Shoulder Yaw -180° +180°

Elbow Pitch -160° +2°

Wrist Pitch +120° -120°

Wrist Yaw -120° +120°

Wrist Roll +/- 447°

Shoulder Pitch -2° +145°

Joint Reference System

X Y Z

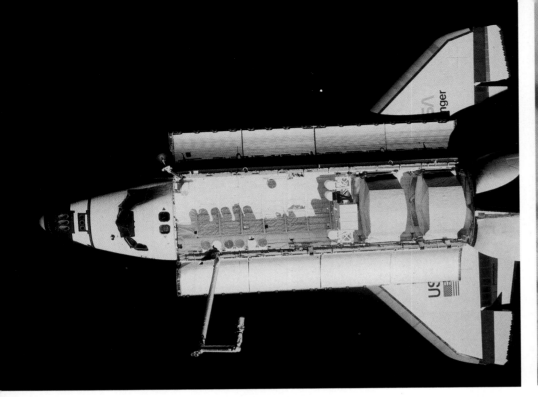

Above Left) CHALLENGER is photographed from the Shuttle Pallet Satellite (SPAS) during STS-7 on 22 June 1983. The Shuttle Remote Manipulator System (SRMS) arm has formed a '7' in honor of the mission. The two containers at the rear of the cargo bay contained Telesat Anik C2 and Palapa B communications satellites. Both satellites were successfully deployed by the STS-7 crew, which included Dr Sally K. Ride, the first American woman to fly in space. (NASA)

Above) A small payload is attached to the grapple of the Shuttle Remote Manipulator System (SRMS). The SRMS is capable of deploying or retrieving payloads up to 65,000 pounds (29,484 KG). The arm has a total weight of 93 pounds (42.2 KG). Astronauts can also use the SRMS as a mobile extension ladder during spacewalks. (NASA)

(Left) The SRMS has six joints which roughly correspond to the human arm in pitch, yaw, and roll. The box just beyond the joint is a video camera for the RCA Astro-Electronics closed-circuit TV system. This camera, along with other cameras in the payload bay, enable astronauts to better handle payloads. Images from these cameras may also be seen on Earth by engineers as well as by the general public. The entire SRMS system, including controllers, weighs 1320 pounds (598.8 KG). (NASA)

(Above) Two Get-Away Special (GAS) canisters are loaded into the starboard side of COLUMBIA's payload bay for STS-90 during 1998. GAS payloads are small experiments carried into space for a fee to NASA by various organizations. The Neurolab payload lies aft of the GAS canisters. Radiators for cooling the Shuttle in orbit line the inside of the payload bay door. (NASA)

(Above Right) Two additional STS-90 Get-Away Specials were loaded into the port side of COLUMBIA's payload bay. Next to the canisters is the Neurolab payload with the tunnel connecting this module to the aft crew cabin. The effects of microgravity on the human nervous system were studied during this mission using Neurolab. This payload is a joint venture between the US, Japan, Canada, France, Germany and the European Space Agency (ESA). (NASA)

(Right) Japanese technicians test the real-time radiation monitoring device aboard SPACEHAB in preparation for STS-89. SPACEHAB is primarily used as a pressurized container for scientific and logistic equipment to be exchanged between the Shuttle and Russia's MIR Space Station. ENDEAVOUR (OV-105) made the eighth docking with MIR on 24 January 1998 while carrying SPACEHAB. (NASA)

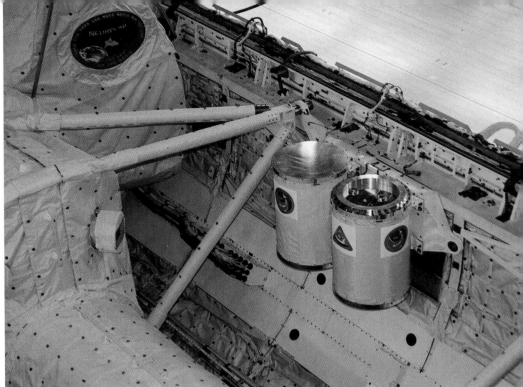

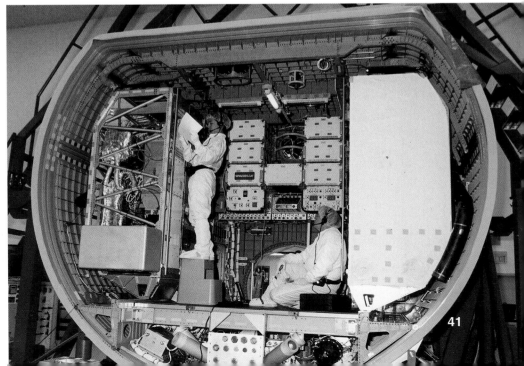

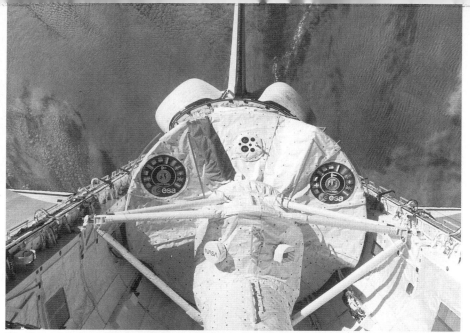

The Spacelab 1 module was first carried into space in the payload bay of COLUMBIA (OV-102) on STS-9 in November of 1983. Spacelab is an orbital laboratory and observations platform composed of cylindrical pressurized modules and U-shaped unpressurized pallets which remain in the Orbiter's cargo bay during the flight. The access tunnel leads to the Shuttle's aft cabin. (NASA)

Story Musgrave moves along the hand rail system on CHALLENGER's starboard side during STS-6 in 1983. Two canisters containing Get-Away Specials (GAS) are placed on the forward payload bay area. Musgrave and Donald Peterson performed the first Shuttle Extravehicular Activity (EVA — space walk) during this mission. (NASA)

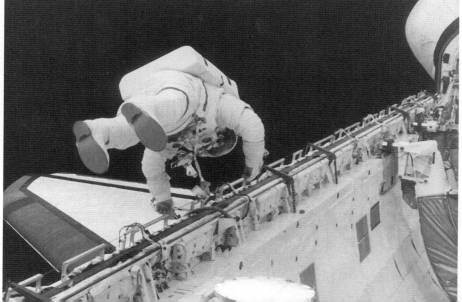

Owen Garriott (foreground) and West Germany's Ulf Merbold work aboard Spacelab during STS-9 in late 1983. Numerous stirrups on the 'floor' are used to anchor Mission Specialists while they work at the consoles under weightless conditions. This mission aboard COLUMBIA was the first to carry Spacelab, a reusable laboratory developed by the European Space Agency (ESA) and NASA. (NASA)

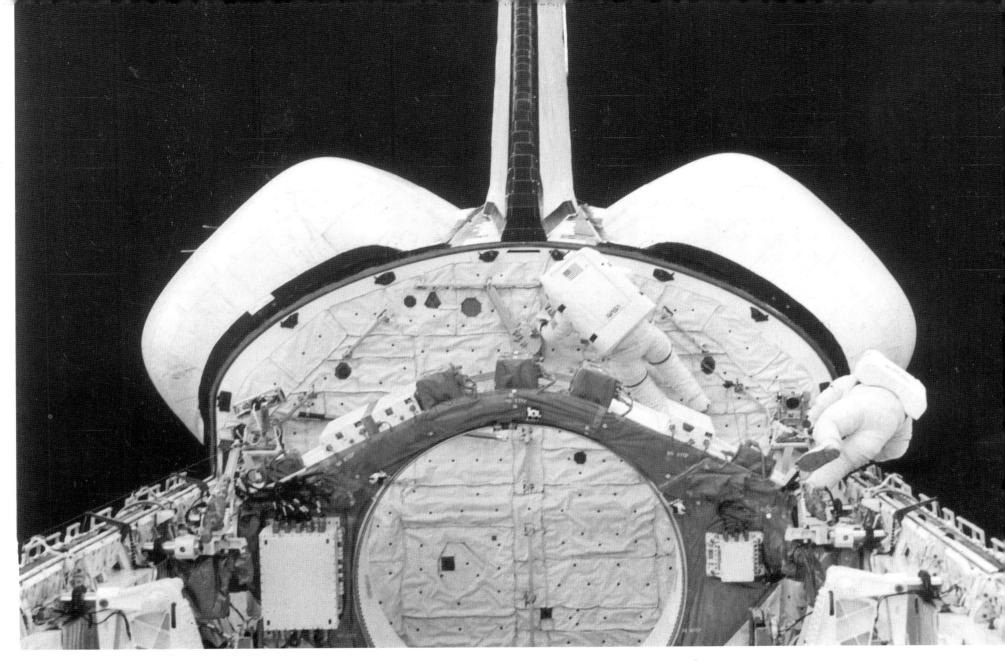

Astronauts Story Musgrave (left) and Donald Peterson work in CHALLENGER's payload bay during STS-6 in April of 1983. The two Payload Specialists are working by the aft section of the 60 foot (18.3 M) long payload bay. They are moving past the bracket which housed the Tracking and Data Relay Satellite prior to its deployment. Musgrave and Peterson spent approximately four hours and 17 minutes on their space walk, in which they successfully tested the EVA suits and hardware for use on future Shuttle missions. The Commander of STS-6 —CHALLENGER's first space flight — was Paul J. Weitz, while Karol J. Bobko was the Pilot. (NASA)

The Remote Manipulator System (RMS) grabs the Shuttle Pallet Satellite (SPAS) in DISCOVERY's payload bay during STS-51 in September of 1993. Next to SPAS is the Orbiting Retrievable Far and Extreme Ultraviolet Spectrometer (ORFEUS), which was deployed using the RMS on 19 September 1993. Two Get-Away Special canisters are placed ahead of the other payloads to port. Astronauts use the wires and handholds running along the sides of the payload bay to assist in moving fore and aft. Payload operator and manufacturer's insignia are common on Shuttle flights due to their publicity value. (NASA)

Commander Joe Engle (left) and Pilot Richard Truly (right) perform a post flight inspection of COLUMBIA after completion of the STS-2 mission on 14 November 1981. The orbiter's wings blend into the forward fuselage through chines, which provide additional wing area. The light gray wing leading edges are composed of Reinforced Carbon-Carbon, which is able to withstand reentry temperatures of 2750° F (1510° C). Black High-Temperature Reusable Surface Insulation (HRSI) tiles cover the landing gear doors and the rest of the Shuttle's under surfaces. Service vehicles have already begun to pump fuel components from the Shuttle's maneuvering systems. (NASA)

COLUMBIA backs out of the Orbiter Processing Facility (OPF) on 16 March 1990, prior to transfer to the nearby VAB. Red covers have been applied to the main engine openings and to the Orbital Maneuvering System (OMS) engine bells. The pod on the top of COLUMBIA's tail houses the Shuttle Infrared Leeside Temperature Sensing (SILTS) experiment, which obtained images of the Shuttle's upper surfaces during reentry for later study. (NASA)

Wing and Tail Perspective

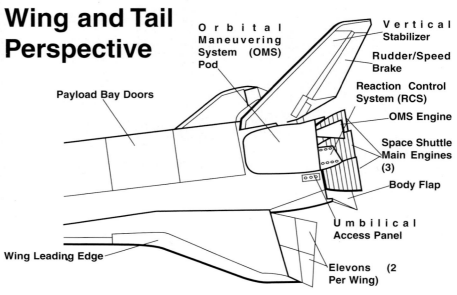

COLUMBIA is lifted by a crane in the Vehicular Assembly Building (VAB) on 3 February 1982. This Shuttle displays the American flag on the port wing and USA on the starboard wing. The other Shuttles have USA and the flag painted on the port wing with the NASA logo and the Shuttle's name on the starboard wing. The Shuttle uses a double-delta wing planform, swept 81° at the inner leading edge and 45° at the outer leading edge. (NASA)

COLUMBIA is raised above the floor of the VAB prior to mating with the External Tank and Solid Rocket Boosters. The three Space Shuttle Main Engines (SSMEs) generate a combined 1,125,000 lbs (510,300 KG) of thrust at sea level. The two Orbital Maneuvering System (OMS) pods surrounding the vertical stabilizer each include an engine capable of generating 6000 lbs (2722 KG) of thrust for adjusting the Shuttle's orbits. Reaction Control System (RCS) thrusters are mounted next to the OMS engines. A body flap under the main engines protects them from reentry heat. A pair of elevons on each wing and the rudder on the vertical stabilizer provides flight control within the Earth's atmosphere. (NASA)

A Rockwell worker paints the American flag on an Orbiter's port wing at the company's Palmdale, California assembly plant. Protective blankets placed on the wing prevent damage to the wing's Thermal Protection System (TPS) elements during final assembly. The paint used for the insignia is Dow Corning 3140 silicon-base material with pigments added, which takes up to 18 hours to dry. This material will break down in temperature ranges of between 800° F (427° C) to 1000° F (538° C). The open panel at the end of States on the fuselage is a payload umbilical panel used to provide external power to payload bay items while the Shuttle is at the launch pad. (Rockwell)

The wing upper surface area near the leading edge is covered in Low-Temperature Reusable Surface Insulation (LRSI), while the rest of the upper wing and aft fuselage are protected with Nomex Felt Reusable Surface Insulation (FRSI). LRSI provides protection against temperatures below 1200° F (649° C), while FRSI offers protection at below 700° F (371° C). (John Rippinger)

The wing leading edges are protected by Reinforced Carbon-Carbon (RCC), which offers protection against reentry temperatures exceeding 2300° F (1260° C). T-seals between each RCC wing panel allow thermal expansion and lateral movement between these panels and the Shuttle's wing. (John Rippinger)

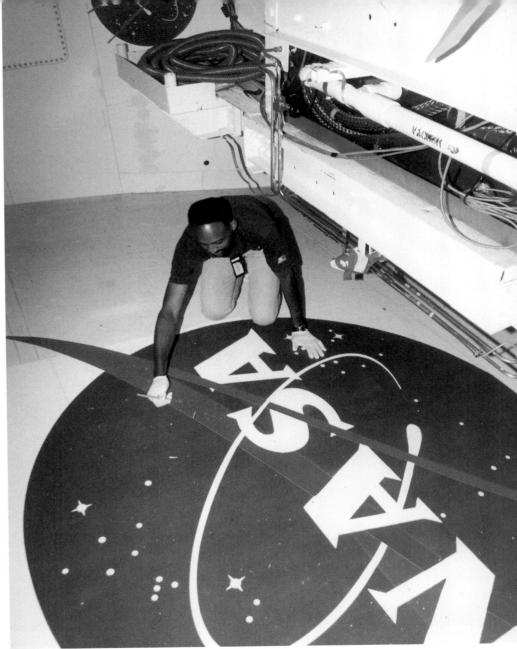

A Kennedy Space Center worker touches up the NASA logo on ENDEAVOUR's port wing during 1998. This emblem has also been applied to the Shuttle's aft fuselage, replacing the earlier NASA 'worm' logo. This 'meatball' logo dates from the 1950s, and was re-adopted in honor of the agency's 40th anniversary in 1998. (NASA)

ENTERPRISE awaits its mating with the External Tank and Solid Rocket Boosters in the VAB's high bay on 24 April 1979. Since this test vehicle was not built to fly into space, ENTERPRISE used polyurethane foam over its aluminum skin to simulate the Thermal Protection System (TPS) tiles used on operational Orbiters. This resulted in ENTERPRISE's vertical stabilizer and upper wing surfaces displaying a different 'color' scheme than on the other Shuttles. (NASA)

ENTERPRISE is removed from the dynamic test stand at the Marshall Space Flight Center in Huntsville, Alabama on 25 August 1978. The smooth black undersurface of ENTERPRISE is due to polyurethane foam, which was used instead of the TPS tiles used on operational Orbiters. The Mated Vertical Ground Vibration Tests, which ENTERPRISE successfully completed, evaluated the Launch Package's integrity under the stresses of launch. (NASA)

Templates are used to install the High-Temperature Reusable Surface Insulation (HRSI) tiles on the undersurface of DISCOVERY during 1982. This painstaking task is done by hand due to the precise tolerances required for each tile. HRSI tiles are made of a low-density, high purity (99.8%) silica fiber insulation made rigid by ceramic bonding. These tiles are also installed on the forward fuselage and the leading edge of the vertical stabilizer. (NASA)

A 250 ton (227 MT) capacity crane suspends COLUMBIA prior to mating the Orbiter with the External Tank (ET) and Solid Rocket Boosters. The vast majority of the Shuttle 20,548 HRSI tiles cover the undersurfaces, providing protection against reentry temperatures ranging from 1200° F to 2300° F. (649° C to 1260° C). The forward ET attachment fixture is located immediately behind the nose landing gear doors. The aft fuselage openings are for electrical, mechanical, and fuel links between the Orbiter and the ET. (NASA)

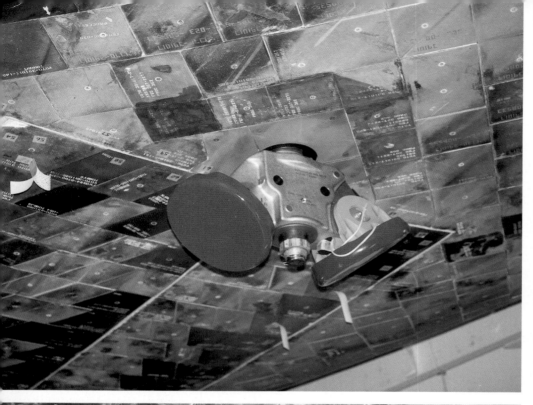

(Above Left) The forward External Tank (ET) attachment fixture is located immediately aft of the nose landing gear doors. Red caps cover the fixture's openings during maintenance. An explosive bolt separates the ET from the Orbiter, and the fixture bearing lies flush with the Orbiter's under surface. To assist maintenance crews with precise placement, the Shuttle's 31,000 thermal tiles are individually labeled. The tiles are applied with special epoxy, which allows them to withstand the structural flexing of extreme temperatures and acoustic shocks of 165 decibels encountered during launch. (John Rippinger)

(Above) Each of the two ET umbilical compartments fitted to the Orbiter's aft under surfaces contains a 17 inch (43.2 см) disconnect. This disconnect contains two flapper valves: one on the orbiter side and one on the external tank side. Both valves in each pair of disconnects are opened to permit propellant flow between the ET and the Orbiter. Inadvertent closure of either valve during main engine thrusting would stop propellant flow from the ET and would result in an immediate shutdown of the main engines. (Lou Drendel)

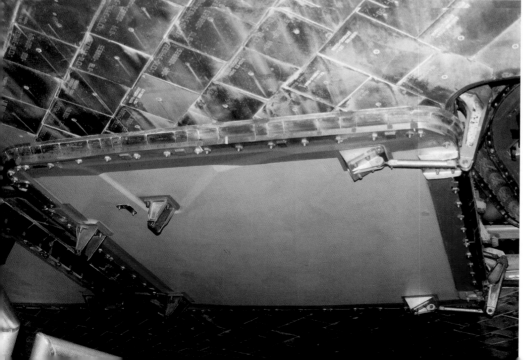

(Left) A door covers each of the two ET umbilical connections when the ET is jettisoned at eight minutes 50 seconds into the flight. Explosive devices separate the umbilicals from the Orbiter, and the doors then close and lock for the remainder of the flight. Each umbilical connection door measures approximately 50 square inches (322.6 см²), and the exterior is covered in HRSI tiles. The umbilical connection door operating speed limit is 17,500 MPH (28,163 кмн)! (Lou Drendel)

(Above) DISCOVERY's port landing gear is extended while the Orbiter was in the Orbiter Processing Facility (OPF) in preparation for a 1998 mission. The two port elevons have drooped without power being applied to these surfaces. Elevon travel range is +40° to −25°, with the maximum deflection rate being 20° per second. The upper elevon surfaces are coated with Nomex Felt Reusable Surface Insulation (FRSI) with Low-Temperature Reusable Surface Insulation (LRSI) along the edges. All lower surfaces are covered with HRSI. The entire structure of the Shuttle is surrounded by a variety of scaffolding and access ladders and ramps during maintenance. (John Rippinger)

(Above Right) The Shuttle's four elevons are connected to the wing by three hinges per elevon. HRSI tiles cover these hinges. Several darker tiles indicate replacements for tiles which were damaged during atmospheric flight. The denser of the two HRSI tile varieties is used on high heat stress areas of the airframe, including doors, the wing leading edge, and the vertical stabilizer leading edge. This tile weights 22 lbs per cubic foot (9.9 KG/M³). The remaining surfaces employing HRSI materials use tiles weighing 9 lbs per cubic foot (4 KG/M³). (John Rippinger)

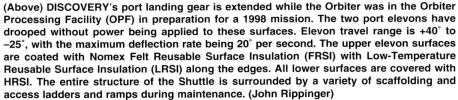

(Right) Each HRSI tile has an identification code painted in yellow. This paint — available commercially under the name Spearex — does not burn off during reentry. One of the tiles displays a slight gouge caused by damage during either ascent or approach and landing. HRSI tiles range in thickness from one to five inches (2.5 CM to 12.7 CM), depending upon the heat load encountered during reentry. Gaps of 0.025 in (0.0635 CM) to 0.065 in (0.165 CM) between each tile prevent tile-to-tile contact due to thermal expansion and contraction. (John Rippinger)

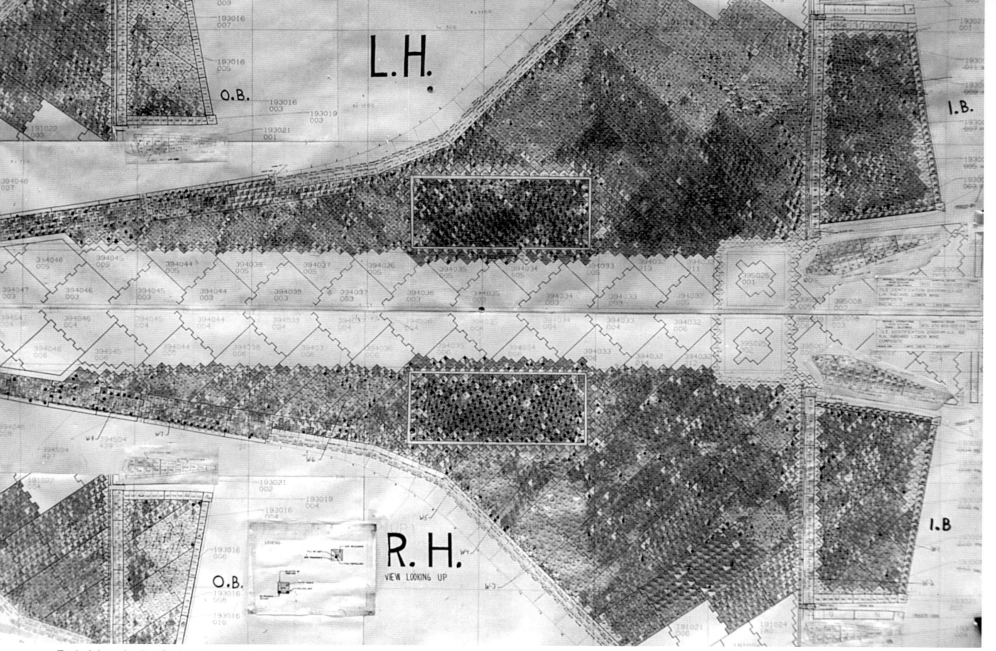

Technicians in the Orbiter Processing Facility at the Kennedy Space Center maintain 1/10th scale layouts of every thermal protection tile on the orbiter, such as this layout for the Orbiter's under surfaces. The layout contains the part number for each of the 31,000 tiles on the Orbiter. A series of numbers for each tile identifies the section of the Orbiter's surface and the location within that section. Each Orbiter's Thermal Protection System (TPS) is carefully inspected after each mission, and damaged or worn tiles are immediately replaced before the next mission. (NASA)

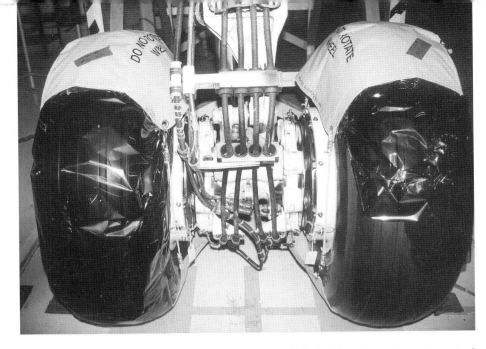

The Michelin 44.5 X 16 main landing gear tires are inflated with nitrogen to a pressure of 315 psi. The tires are covered during maintenance to prevent fluid spills on the tires, which normally last for five landings. The maximum allowable weight per main gear tire is 123,000 lbs (55,793 KG). Hydraulic lines for the brakes and gear operation run down the back of the gear leg. (John Rippinger)

Main Landing Gear

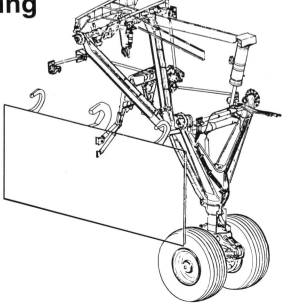

The main landing gears retract forward into the gear bays located in the inboard wing surfaces. A single door constructed from aluminum alloy honeycomb covers each gear bay. The flight crew can fully extend the landing gear in ten seconds during the landing approach.(NASA)

Maintenance crews have erected a ladder in front of the landing gear to examine the port main landing gear bay. The landing gear door retracts inward from its outboard hinge to totally enclose the gear bay. The gear doors contain seals to prevent excessive temperature and pressure changes to the landing gear during space flight. (John Rippinger.)

The main gear shock struts are of conventional hydraulic design. These struts use a combination of hydraulic fluid and gaseous nitrogen, which must be separated by a diaphragm to prevent mixing in zero g conditions. Max extension speed is 345 mph (555 кмн), which normally occurs below 250 feet (76.2 м). (John Rippinger)

The main landing gear struts retract forward into the landing gear bays. Piping on the strut carries hydraulic fluid to the brakes. The gear strut components are manufactured from high strength stress and corrosion resistant steel and aluminum alloys, stainless steel, and aluminum bronze. The landing gear extends down and to the rear. (John Rippinger)

The steel interiors of the landing gear bays are covered with cadmium-titanium plating for heat resistance purposes. Hydraulic lines run through the bay from fluid tanks within the mid-fuselage. The white struts are part of the landing gear assembly. (John Rippinger.)

Landing gear surfaces are coated with white urethane paint or cadmium-titanium plating. The gear operates by a combination of hydraulic pressure and gravity. In the event of hydraulic loss, a pyrotechnic initiator opens the gear doors to allow the gear to free fall into position. Anti-skid brakes assist with directional control during crosswind landings. (John Rippinger)

The ribs around the three Space Shuttle Main Engine (SSME) bells are propellant circulation tubes for cooling the engines prior to the propellant — liquid hydrogen and liquid oxygen — being burned. Each Orbital Maneuvering System (OMS) pod includes one OMS engine, 12 Reaction Control System (RCS) primary thrusters, and two RCS vernier thrusters. The OMS provides thrust for orbital maneuvers, including insertion, circularization, transfer, rendezvous, abort to orbit, and abort once around. The launch umbilical panel is located on the aft fuselage below the RCS thrusters, while an aft fuselage access panel is forward of the umbilical panel. (NASA)

Advanced Flexible Reusable Surface Insulation (AFRSI) blankets are applied to one of DISCOVERY's Orbiter Maneuvering System (OMS) pods at Palmdale. The low-density fibrous silica batting material results in the OMS pod's surface having a quilt-like appearance. Each OMS pod contains one OMS engine and the hardware needed to pressurize, store, and distribute the propellants to perform velocity maneuvers. (Rockwell)

Orbital Maneuvering System (OMS)

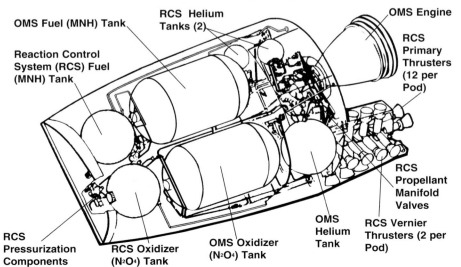

OMS Fuel (MNH) Tank

RCS Helium Tanks (2)

Reaction Control System (RCS) Fuel (MNH) Tank

OMS Engine

RCS Primary Thrusters (12 per Pod)

RCS Propellant Manifold Valves

RCS Pressurization Components

RCS Oxidizer (N_2O_4) Tank

OMS Oxidizer (N_2O_4) Tank

OMS Helium Tank

RCS Vernier Thrusters (2 per Pod)

The port OMS pod is lowered into position during the construction of COLUMBIA (OV-102) during 1980. The circles on the sides of the pod are Reaction Control System (RCS) thrusters, employed for normal translation and altitude control. (NASA)

DISCOVERY is backed out of the Orbiter Processing Facility on 7 July 1997. Foreign Object Damage (FOD) covers have been placed on the main and OMS engines. Two cylinders protruding from the rear of each OMS pod are primary Reaction Control System thrusters. The body flap underneath the two lower main engines protects the engines from reentry heat. (NASA)

A new Rocketdyne Block 2A Space Shuttle Main Engine (SSME) sits on a workstand at the Kennedy Space Center in 1998. This engine, introduced in 1985, offers greater reliability than the earlier Block 1 SSMEs. The large pipe wrapping around the engine is a pogo (up-and-down vibration) DFI (Developmental Flight Instrumentation) connector, which prevents thrust oscillation from adversely affecting engine performance. (NASA)

The starboard orbital maneuvering system (OMS) engine is covered to prevent Foreign Object Damage (FOD) during maintenance. Two cylindrical Reaction Control System (RCS) thrusters are placed to the right of the OMS engine, while an OMS control panel is next to the engine base. (John Rippinger)

The pipe running along the length of the upper main engine bell is a propellant vent, while the series of parallel pipes used propellant to cool the engine nozzle. The port OMS engine bell is near the main engine. (John Rippinger)

High-Temperature Reusable Surface Insulation (HRSI) tiles provide a thermal barrier around the main engine mounts. These tiles are removed when the main engines are pulled off for servicing. The main engines can be throttled between 67% and 109%, although 104% is the normal maximum setting used on flights. Ignition occurs 6.6 seconds before liftoff, and cutoff is at 507 seconds into the flight. (John Rippinger)

Four of the RCS primary thrusters used for attitude control are mounted on the outboard side of the port OMS pod. Maintenance scaffolding obscures the port umbilical panel, which is used to import electrical power to the Shuttle from the launch pad. (John Rippinger)

Plugs protruding from each RCS primary thruster are attached to thruster opening covers. These covers are designed to keep Foreign Object Damage out of the thrusters during Shuttle maintenance. (John Rippinger)

The seven circles on the side of COLUMBIA's port Orbital Maneuvering System (OMS) pod are Reaction Control System (RCS) primary thrusters. The small hole next to the top row of thrusters is an RCS vernier thruster, used for fine attitude control of the Shuttle. Two additional primary thrusters are outboard of the OMS engine. A dark OMS pod service panel is next to the bottom row of thrusters, above and aft of the umbilical panel. (NASA)

Rudder and Speed Brake Travel

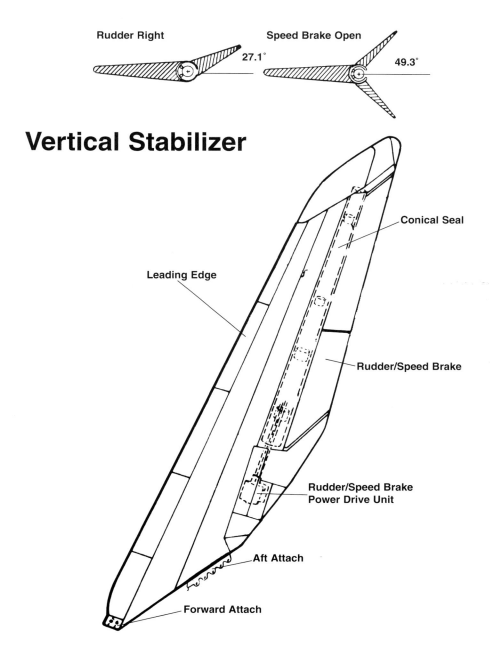

Rudder Right

Speed Brake Open

27.1°

49.3°

Vertical Stabilizer

Conical Seal

Leading Edge

Rudder/Speed Brake

Rudder/Speed Brake Power Drive Unit

Aft Attach

Forward Attach

Technicians lower the vertical stabilizer onto ENTERPRISE's aft fuselage at Palmdale in 1976. The rudder/speed brake has 27° of travel left or right of center when used as the rudder. When the rudder is split to act as a speed brake, the individual halves travel up to 49.3° off center. White polyurethane foam covers portions of the stabilizer's aluminum skin. The stabilizer's leading edge is swept back at a 45° angle. (Rockwell)

Workers use cables to hoist the vertical stabilizer for DISCOVERY at Rockwell's Palmdale plant. The four elevons — two per wing — for this shuttle are also nearing completion. These elevons employ conventional aluminum multi-rib and beam construction with aluminum honeycomb skins. The rudder/speed brake and the elevons provide the Shuttle's only control during descent and landing. (Rockwell)

DISCOVERY'S completed vertical stabilizer/rudder is prepared for mating with the Orbiter's aft fuselage at Palmdale. The rudder/speed brake was constructed in upper and lower sections which were joined together. The black demarcation between the rudder and the vertical fin is the conical seal hiding four rotary actuators. Thermal Protection System (TPS) elements have not yet been applied to this stabilizer. (Rockwell)

The speed brake is deployed as Commander Charles Precourt brings DISCOVERY back to Kennedy Space Center (KSC) at the completion of STS-91 on 12 June 1998. In addition to the speed brake, the pilots employ aerodynamic braking to help slow down the Orbiter. The Shuttle's speed is reduced from 424 mph (682.3 кмн) at 10,000 feet (3048 м) — when the approach and landing phase begins — to approximately 215 mph (346 кмн) at touchdown. The Shuttle Landing Facility at KSC measures 15,000 feet (4572 м) in length, with 1000 foot (305 м) overruns at both ends. The runway is 300 feet (91.4 м) wide, and 16 inches (40.6 см) thick at the centerline. (NASA)

A Mobile Launch Platform (MLP) carrying COLUMBIA approaches launch position at Pad 39A on 16 February 1982 for STS-3. Once the MLP is set into place on the pad, the Crawler/Transporter returns to the Vehicle Assembly Building 3.5 miles (5.6 KM) away. The Rotating Service Structure (RSS) will enclose the Orbiter to provide access and services on the launch pad. Umbilical lines and the crew access arm will be extended from the taller Fixed Service Structure to the Orbiter. The base of the launch pad contains 68,000 cubic yards (51,990 M³) of concrete. (NASA via Robert F. Dorr)

Thousands of gallons of water gush from six large quench nozzles onto the deck of the Mobile Launcher Platform during a test of the Sound Suppression System. This system reduces the noise levels at the pad on launch, and cools down the launch pad from the intense heat of the Main Engines and Solid Rocket Boosters. The crew access arm has been extended from the Fixed Service Structure to the Orbiter's access hatch. (NASA)

COLUMBIA clears the tower of Pad 39A on 27 June 1982. This launch began STS-4, the last of four developmental test flights prior to the Shuttle fleet being declared fully operational. The Shuttle's three main engines employ thrust vectoring for liftoff control. The Shuttle rolls 120° to starboard upon clearing the Fixed Service Structure, placing the External Tank on top during the remainder of the ascent. (NASA)

A 70mm camera on board the free-flying Shuttle Pallet Satellite (SPAS-01) captures CHAL-LENGER on 22 June 1983, during the STS-7 mission. The Shuttle Remote Manipulator System (SRMS) is extended out from the forward payload bay area. The protective cradles in the aft portion of the payload bay housed the Telesat Anik C2 and Palapa 6 communications satellites deployed earlier on this mission. After approximately nine hours of formation flight, CHALLENGER retrieved SPAS-01 for the return to Earth. (NASA)

Astronaut Bruce McCandless II operates the Manned Maneuvering Unit (MMU) from CHAL-LENGER during STS-41-B on 7 February 1984. This first use of the MMU was also the first untethered space walk in history. A crewmember uses rotational and translational hand controllers on the nitrogen-propelled backpack unit to fly with precision in or around the Shuttle payload bay. McCandless flew the MMU on 7 and 8 February, going up to 300 ft (91.4 M) from CHALLENGER. (NASA)

Robert Stewart flies the MMU from CHALLENGER during STS-41-B. A video camera is mounted above his right shoulder. He wears the Extravehicular Mobility Unit (EMU), a modular spacewalk suit with interchangeable parts. These parts — including the upper torso, lower torso, arms, and gloves — are manufactured in different sizes to fit men and women. (NASA)

McCandless attaches the docking test trunnion pin attachment device (grappling tool) to the Shuttle Pallet Satellite (SPAS) in CHALLENGER's payload bay. The upper torso of the EVA spacesuit is a hard-shell fiberglass structure which contains the primary life support system and the display control module. (NASA)

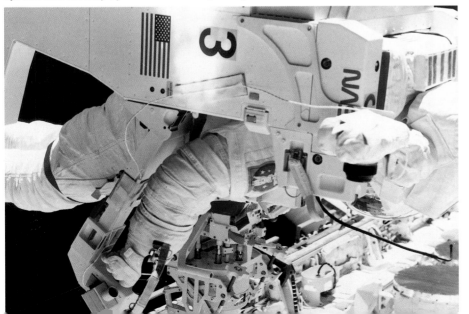

McCandless tests the mobile foot restraints on the SRMS while above the payload bay. The EMU is rated with a minimum 8-year life expectancy, with a nominal operating atmospheric pressure of 4.3 psi. The gold-lined faceplate protects the astronaut's eyes from the intense rays of the sun. Bearings in the shoulder, arm, wrist, and waist joints allow the crewmember freedom of movement. The entire suit assembly weighs 107 pounds (48.5 KG). (NASA)

Commander John Young (left) and Pilot Bob Crippen flew COLUMBIA on the first Shuttle mission, STS-1, during April of 1981. Launched from the Kennedy Space Center on 12 April, Young and Crippen conducted tests of the Shuttle's performance over a two-day period. COLUMBIA carried a Developmental Flight Instrumentation (DFI) payload to measure temperatures, acceleration, and pressures throughout the vehicle. The maiden flight of a spacecraft piloted by astronauts ended with a successful landing at Edwards Air Force Base on 14 April. Young — a veteran of two Gemini and two Apollo missions — commanded COLUMBIA on STS-41-A during 1983. CRIPPEN commanded STS-7 in 1983 and STS-41-G in 1984 — both aboard CHALLENGER. (NASA)

Astronaut Story Musgrave works in the cargo bay of CHALLENGER during STS-6 in April of 1983. Musgrave is working beside the bracket used to hold the first Tracking and Data Relay Satellite (TDRS-A), deployed earlier in this mission. The TDRS — one of four used to relay communications between ground control and spacecraft in orbit —reached its assigned orbit two months after deployment. Musgrave and Donald Peterson performed the first Extravehicular Activity (EVA; i.e., spacewalk) of the Shuttle program, which lasted four hours 17 minutes. Musgrave subsequently flew on three other Shuttle missions, including STS-61 during 1993, He performed repairs on the Shuttle-deployed Hubble Space Telescope on that mission. (NASA)

North American X-15A-2 (56-6671) was the second of three X-15s built for high speed and high altitude research. External propellant tanks were mounted under the chines of this aircraft, resulting in greater endurance.

The Boeing X-20 Dyna-Soar was intended to serve as a reusable space vehicle for military missions. The X-20 project had reached the mock-up stage when it was cancelled in 1963.

The Martin Marietta X-24A (66-13551) performed low speed handling tests of the lifting body concept between 1969 and 1971.

Martin Marietta X-24B (66-13551) was modified from the X-24A to perform high speed lifting body testing.

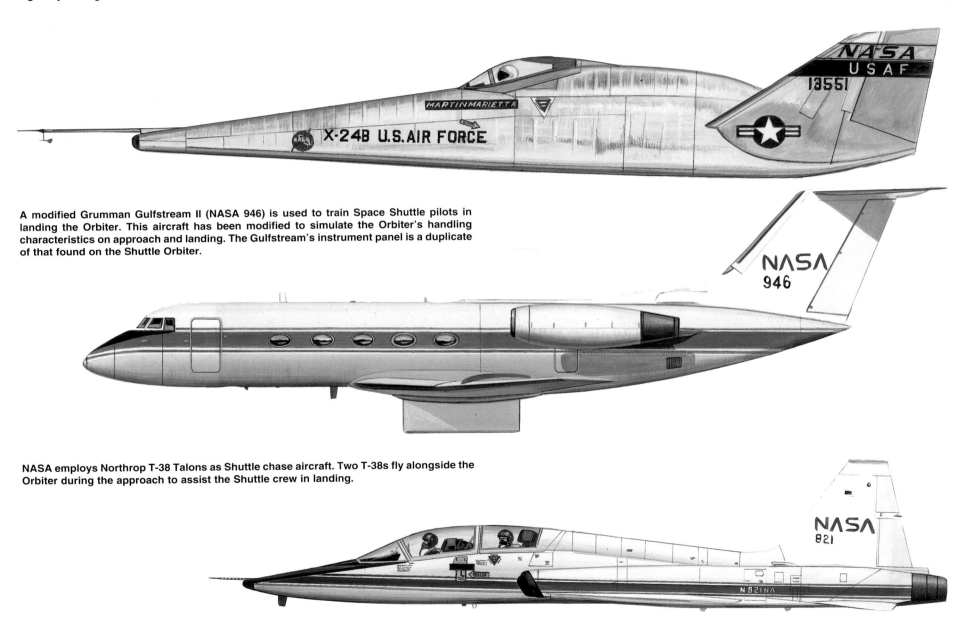

A modified Grumman Gulfstream II (NASA 946) is used to train Space Shuttle pilots in landing the Orbiter. This aircraft has been modified to simulate the Orbiter's handling characteristics on approach and landing. The Gulfstream's instrument panel is a duplicate of that found on the Shuttle Orbiter.

NASA employs Northrop T-38 Talons as Shuttle chase aircraft. Two T-38s fly alongside the Orbiter during the approach to assist the Shuttle crew in landing.

COLUMBIA begins its approach to Edwards Air Force Base, California at the completion of STS-2 on 14 November 1981. At 86 seconds to touchdown, the Shuttle is at 10,000 feet (3048 м) altitude, 7.5 miles (12.1 км) to the runway, and flying at a speed of 424 mph (682.3 кмн). One of NASA's two T-38 chase aircraft is flying port of the Shuttle to assist COLUMBIA's crew with landing. John Young flew the other chase aircraft from where this photograph was taken. Commander Joe Engle and Pilot Richard Truly maintained control using only the Shuttle's rudder and elevons. COLUMBIA landed safely at Edwards after a two-day flight. (NASA)

CHALLENGER returns to Edwards AFB after STS-6 on 9 April 1983, accompanied by a T-38 (NASA 923) chase aircraft. NASA's T-38s feature larger speedbrakes than on US Air Force versions to allow Shuttle chase pilots to fly these missions. The landing gear is deployed while the Shuttle is flying at 267 mph (429.7 KMH) and 89 feet (27.1 M) of altitude.

The Shuttle touches down at 215 mph (346 KMH). The crew uses aerodynamic braking to slow down the vehicle before applying the Orbiter's anti-skid brakes. The Kennedy Space Center runway is nearly 3 miles (4.8 KM) long, while the longest runway at Edwards is 7.5 miles (12.1 KM) long. (NASA)

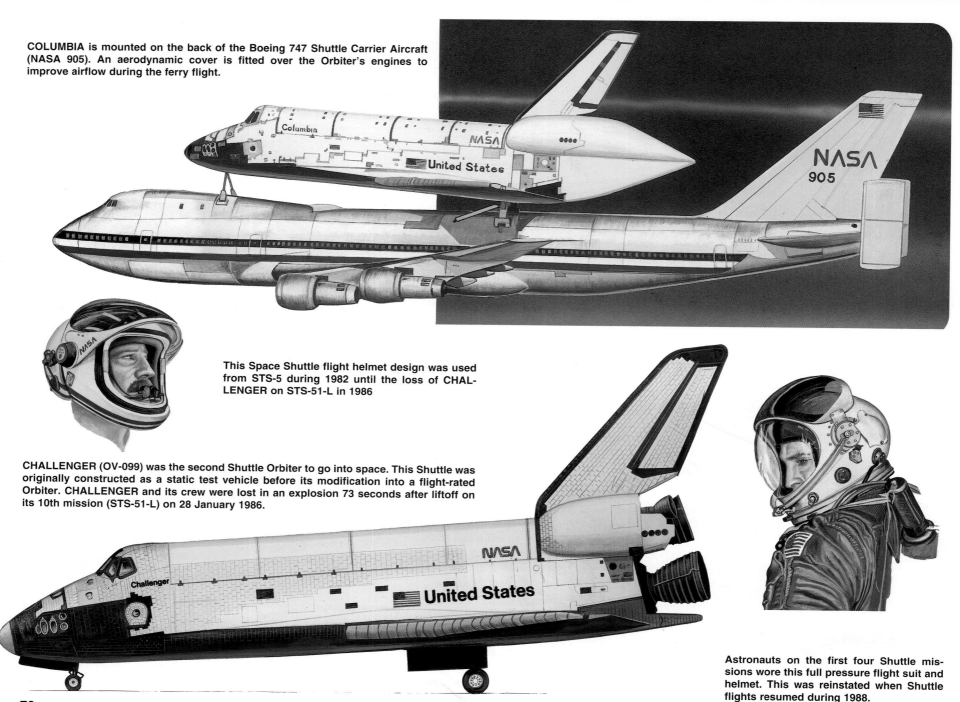

COLUMBIA is mounted on the back of the Boeing 747 Shuttle Carrier Aircraft (NASA 905). An aerodynamic cover is fitted over the Orbiter's engines to improve airflow during the ferry flight.

This Space Shuttle flight helmet design was used from STS-5 during 1982 until the loss of CHALLENGER on STS-51-L in 1986

CHALLENGER (OV-099) was the second Shuttle Orbiter to go into space. This Shuttle was originally constructed as a static test vehicle before its modification into a flight-rated Orbiter. CHALLENGER and its crew were lost in an explosion 73 seconds after liftoff on its 10th mission (STS-51-L) on 28 January 1986.

Astronauts on the first four Shuttle missions wore this full pressure flight suit and helmet. This was reinstated when Shuttle flights resumed during 1988.

The Space Shuttle Orbiter CHALLENGER is depicted in the standard Shuttle launch configuration. Primary liftoff thrust is provided by the two recoverable Solid Rocket Boosters. Secondary thrust comes from the three Space Shuttle Main Engines, fed with liquid hydrogen and liquid oxygen propellants from the orange External Tank. From the launch of COLUMBIA on STS-1 on 12 April 1981 through the middle of 1999, 95 Shuttle missions have been carried out.

COLUMBIA touches down on the Rogers Dry Lake runway at Edwards Air Force Base at the completion of STS-9 (41-A) on 8 December 1983. The fuselage sides and Orbital Maneuvering System pods display staining due to reentry heat on the Thermal Protection System tiles. The Orbiter uses a variety of landing aids, including Tactical Air Navigation (TACAN). The Shuttle can receive TACAN data at an altitude of 145,000 feet (44,196 м) to assist in setting up the approach. COLUMBIA used White Sands Missile Range in New Mexico as a landing site for the conclusion of STS-3 during 1982, due to flooding at Rogers Dry Lake. White Sands was the only Shuttle landing venue used apart from Edwards AFB and the Kennedy Space Center (KSC). (NASA)

DISCOVERY rolls out at KSC with speed brakes and drag chute deployed. The drag chute is deployed once the nose gear touches down at about 185 knots. The drag chute is 40 feet (12.2 M) in diameter and is automatically jettisoned as the Orbiter slows through 60 knots. Landing aids at KSC include the Microwave Scanning Beam Landing System (MSBLS), which provides an automatic landing capability. (NASA)

COLUMBIA has rolled to a stop at Edwards and will be approached from behind by ground safing personnel. The Shuttle travels just over 5000 ft (1524 M) from main landing gear touchdown to wheel stop. A convoy of up to 30 vehicles and 150 personnel are responsible for purging toxic gases from the Shuttle, including hydrogen, monomethyl hydrazine, nitrogen tetroxide and hydrazine, and ammonia. (NASA)

John Glenn checks his gloves in KSC's Operations and Checkout Building prior to STS-95. Glenn, the first American to orbit the Earth, flew aboard DISCOVERY during a 1998 mission. He conducted experiments on the effects of space travel on the aging process. At age 77, Glenn became the oldest person to fly into space — 36 years and eight months after his previous space flight on the Mercury spacecraft Friendship 7. (NASA)

Lou Drendel has been associated with Squadron/Signal Publications since 1972, writing and illustrating over 50 books in several different series. His illustrations have also appeared in The Chicago Tribune Magazine, Time-Life Publications, Berkely Books, and several other publications. Lou also provides illustrations for the American Flyers, Inc. website.

In addition to his writing and painting, Lou is a Commercial Pilot and lead solo of the Lima Lima Flight Team. (www.limalima.com) Lima Lima was the first six-airplane civilian aerobatic formation team in the world. It has flown hundreds of performances in front of millions of spectators, from coast-to-coat and border-to-border in the 12 years of its existence. Lou was a founding member of the team and is the current business manager. The Lima Lima Flight Team flies the Beech T-34 Mentor, a 1950s vintage primary trainer, which was used by the Navy, USAF, and foreign governments. (See the author's T-34 in Action, Aircraft Number 107, published by Squadron/Signal Publications.) There are approximately 300 T-34s on the civil register. Lou is president of the national T-34 Association, an owner support organization which publishes a quarterly magazine devoted to T-34 issues. (www.T-34.com)

Lou is also a regional sales manager for the Edward Hines Lumber Company, the largest supplier of building materials to professional builders in the Chicago metro area. He is a director of the Northern Illinois Home Builders Association. Lou and wife Carol live in Naper Aero Estates, a residential airpark Southwest of Chicago. They have three children and one grandchild.